Shelter

Notes from a Detained Migrant Children's facility

Cover Art Esmeralda Piza

Luna Triste Press

Luna Triste Press, LLC
PO Box 10280 Phoenix 85064-0280
602.325.1224
marketing@lunitabooks.com

ISBN: 978-1-7346843-1-5 (Ingram)
ISBN: 978-1-7346843-0-8 (Amazon)
LunitaBooks.Com

All characters in this book are
fictional composites.
They do not correspond to specific
children or incidents.

For my daughters,
Anais and Ixchel

May you meet with kindness on
your journey

Shelter

Notes from a Detained Migrant Children's facility

One

To me, the congressman outside our shelter had no idea what he was asking. We knew why he had been blocked at the gate. Inside, hundreds of children waited, studied, cried, called home, went to school and the dentist, learned to paint and play chess. Many had suffered trauma and were fleeing those who did them harm. What we did as a shelter was done carefully. No one just entered our building.

I scanned my ID at the security door, turned the corner and stood before a row of kids in folding chairs. They were waiting for the nurse.

"Are you all ready for shots?"

The one girl was stoic, the half dozen boys not as much.

"They say we'll get nine," said a boy with excited eyes.

"They don't hurt," I replied. "Except for this one," and I pointed to the side of my neck.

All the boy eyes got bigger, but the sole girl giggled. "There are no neck shots, you dummies."

They had taken journeys best done in the bravery of youth, but for all that, they were still kids. I'd got them. An embarrassed laughter erupted.

The group had been dropped off the previous night. Every evening, the ICE vans delivered new children, and I looked forward each morning to bantering and making the situation less intimidating.

"What time did you get in?"

"They didn't tell us," replied the girl. "But everyone was asleep. We didn't know where we were going."

"Did you all have breakfast?"

"Yes. The tortillas taste funny."

"We don't make them by hand like your mom. But the food is good. You'll like it."

The boy who seemed oldest, maybe sixteen, jumped into the conversation. "I don't want to be here. I'm just going to my dad."

I could tell he had been crying.

"Mijo, everyone cries when they get here, and they all cry when they leave. You'll have fun. Parents take the least work for us, but there is a lot to do."

"My friend told me that his friend was going to his mom and got out in one day."

"Exaggeration," said the girl. "You're in someone else's country. It's not that easy."

I told the group that after the nurse, they would meet their case worker and she or he would let them call home. "This is the last part of your journey. Patience."

Patience would come around the fourth day. Until then, that specific virtue would take a back seat to frustration, tears, and the anxious vigilance appropriate to feeling trapped.

I stopped in across the hall and entered the medical isolation room. One of the case managers, a twenty-three-year-old spitfire of a woman, sat by the sick bed of our client, and I placed my chair next to her. Osby, a diminutive twelve-year-old had arrived months earlier with his brother Ezequias. The sibling had now been released, leaving Osby behind.

Every Wednesday, the supervisor from the Office of Refugee Resettlement stopped by and reviewed the status of every child in the shelter. Each case manager presented the extensive paperwork gathered thus far, client by client. When it came to Osby's brother, the new ORR supervisor had said it wasn't possible to retain a child cleared for exit, even if that meant leaving a sibling behind.

"Didn't the hospital say that Osby could travel after the tests?"

"Yes, they did," said the case manager. "But Ellen, that new ORR lady, won't let him go. His parents hesitated when the hospital asked to put a tube in Osby's heart. She said that means they're not safe. She wants a social worker to see them."

"Hijole, you get a scary call asking to do weird things to your kid. Who doesn't ask questions?"

"Well, she also said the parents have four kids in one house and that's enough. He has to live with his married brother."

We just looked at each other.

"We were nine at my house," she added.

"I wish the old ORR guy would come back. We need his New York street sense."

Osby was tiny, but an excellent soccer player, quick in school and a pure stoic. Since leaving third grade, he had managed all the farming on his grandparents' plot in Guatemala. He and Ezequias spent three weeks making their way to the U.S. border, and Osby began suffering dizzy spells on the buses. Since arriving at the shelter, he had been hospitalized twice. Each stay involved injections, tubes, a variety of invasive tests and one small surgery. Yet, no one had seen Osby cry or complain, even as nurses pushed tubes down his throat. Whenever we asked how he felt, his only answer was "Bien."

"Osby," I said. "You're going to live on a farm close to your parents. You can stop for breakfast on the way to school. Montana is cold right now, so maybe it's good you're still here."

"When can I go back to my class? Friday, we show our projects."

Osby let me know that his father was the supervisor of horses and cattle, and that the married brother drove and fixed machines on the farm. He had not seen his parents in ten years, but they spoke on the phone. One after the other, each of the children had made their way to Montana. He was last, and he was "Bien."

Reggaeton was blasting from the yard, and the three of us could see the girls'soccer game through a long one-way window installed in medical isolation. These were eight-minute games before the next teams received their soccer time. Around the small field, kids were boxing, skipping rope, lifting weights and learning dances. The recreation leaders constantly invented all manner of activities to keep several hundred tweens and teens occupied and exercised.

Right in front of our window, a girl gave a fist bump to a boy as she walked past.

"Did you see that?" asked the case manager.

"She passed a note to Clinton. She likes him," said Osby from his bed.

"Fist bumps will soon disappear," I said. "I'm sure the youth workers are onto this note thing."

Some shelters did not allow male and female clients to have any interaction or occupy the same space. Those shelters often had reprimands if a boy looked to long at the girls passing on their way to lunch or recreation. Our shelter allowed interaction. Boys and girls were in classrooms together and for certain activities like art and music, they could talk freely. However, and this was strictly enforced, there was no touching of any kind except for fist bumps. There was no sharing of letters, no handshakes or hugs, no giving of gifts and personal articles. On Friday nights, we had dances, and the line of boys danced with the line of girls in front of them. But again, no touching.

In a fluid, emotional and stressful situation, teens falling in love and claiming boyfriends or girlfriends would have led to drama, physical fights and infighting. While giving the kids as much normalcy as possible, this was not a normal situation, and without strict enforcement of rules and boundaries, the social atmosphere would have become volatile and unsafe. In their already precarious legal situation, any violence or bad behavior impacted their chance of joining family.

Still, they fell in love and made secret pacts to find each other. One of the case managers said that's exactly how her own parents met.

Leaving Osby, I made my way to a fifth-floor office. The elevator was out permanently, so the wellness committee had posted signs praising our stamina and commitment to personal health.

In my counseling office, a teen boy and a taller girl stood at my computer. Guatemalan children never sat unless asked to by adults, and never while the adult still stood.

"The case worker dropped them off," said my office mate. "She's done and the nurse said you have thirty minutes before she needs them."

If children arrived at night, they were provided sleepwear and taken to a first-night bed, and we were not to wake them for eight hours. Exhausted from the road and their few nights confined to an immigration jail, they usually slept the sound, hard sleep of all children. But once up, the clock began. We had twenty-four hours to vaccinate, provide clothing, get full background, call home and call their sponsoring relative in the U.S. If any concerns arose during this process—trauma or medical issues revealed—we had four hours to report and address them. We had much to do beside take in new arrivals, and those other tasks were also timed. If you were professional staff, you went home when the work was done, and on the worst days, we could look forward to watching over a frightened kid in a hospital room till the next morning.

"Los niños . . . hablan . . . nomas Kiche." The children speak only Kiche. My Mormon colleague had acquired Spanish on

a mission to Ecuador. His slow, enunciated sentences endeared him to his clients.

"I understand everything," said the boy in accented Spanish.

I asked them to take a chair.

"Efren, your Spanish is good. Did you learn it in school?"

"Some, but I learned more on the road."

I turned to his sister who was looking attentive, her eyes bright and energetic.

"She's deaf and can't talk. She doesn't read or write."

Does she know how to sign?

"No. That's why they made her come with me. She works and takes care of animals, but there's no school for her."

The deaf teen's gaze, direct and absorbing, jumped between faces as we spoke. "My father knows she'll never get married, and someone will take advantage of her."

On my computer screen were the background questions from the Office of Refugee Resettlement, the branch of Homeland Security that watched over the shelters.

"Today is going to be busy. I need to ask questions so the government can start your process. I'm going to be your counselor. I'll also help the case manager get you to family."

"How long will we be here?"

"We're not supposed to give you an exact time. Your case manager will ask you to be patient because they can't promise anything. But if your uncle and parents give us all the papers we need, and they get fingerprinted fast, and nothing goes wrong, it usually takes about forty days."

"What can go wrong?"

"Someone in the house doesn't have an ID anymore or won't give it to us. Maybe your uncle already sponsored other kids and they didn't do what they were supposed to. Or it takes a while to find all the birth certificates. Little things, but each one adds time."

"Nothing will go wrong."

"That's my hope. But you won't remember if it took one month or two. Try to make this a good memory. Are you ready? We have to go quickly."

"Yes."

"How did you get to the United states?"

Efren turned to his sister and gestured a walk with his fingers, and she nodded back.

"Her name is Dayeli," Efren said. "But she doesn't know that. Unless you teach her to write. Then she'll know it that way."

He answered all the questions about the journey, their previous life, school, family and the work done on the farm. I had to separate the siblings for questions related to trauma, sex or abuse. My office mate watched over Efren while I took Dayeli to an adjacent interview room. I had prints from class presentations on child abuse and showed Dayeli a picture of a parent threatening a child, and then one more print of a young woman fending off an advance. Dayeli immediately shook her head "no" when I pointed to the pages and then to her. That was as best for now. I would have to rely on her brother's version of history and any signs of emotional trauma in the coming days.

I walked them down to the nurse for vaccinations and then crossed the outdoor field to one of the classrooms.

I asked the youth worker at the door of Classroom D if I could take Candelaria to weekly counseling. Youth workers were the unsung heroes of the shelter. All day long, they watched over and motivated, exercised, drove, played with and were responsible for hundreds of kids. At night, they stayed up and checked on every child every fifteen minutes. In the classroom, their main job was to be vigilant and make sure students were not touching, passing notes, harming themselves, or picking on classmates. For students on "close observation," the youth workers took note every fifteen minutes of changes in mood or behavior, and some had been assigned to follow one youth for the entire day. The job was physically and emotionally taxing, and often tedious and stressful. They were taken to task if anything went wrong. Yet, few ever quit.

I knew security was scanning the classrooms, so I waved to the camera before exiting with Candelaria. The shelter placed cameras throughout, for the children's' safety and for our own.

Every job has taught me something obvious which I had never considered. Here I learned that it is tough to prove two people are related: a brother or sister requires birth certificates with the exact parental name on both. Not hard. But to prove an uncle requires the uncle's and the related parent's birth certificates; a first cousin requires grandparents and a second cousin, great-grandparents. Personally, I have never seen my parents' birth certificates, and finding my dad's would mean a trip to a small village in Mexico. My grandparents' would be impossible.

The kids coming to the shelters were not from cities. They were from the Mayan highlands and valleys. Most lived in handmade shelters without plumbing or electricity. Twenty years ago, Guatemala began computerizing birth records, but anything before that was kept by each village in some official cabinet. The parents told me those cabinets were often emptied to make room for new documents. Fires, weather and earthquakes added to the destruction. And how important was an old birth certificate? Especially if the person was now buried?

At the shelter, we needed to prove that a brother, cousin, or uncle wanting to sponsor was truly a relative. It took heroic effort by case managers and people back home to do this. Often, a parent traveled hundreds of miles to a state capital hoping the government had kept a record. It always cost money. Most parents lived on fifty cents a day, so a ten-dollar fax or fifty-dollar journey meant borrowing or selling the little they owned. Often, nothing turned up.

And sometimes, when it did, the names on the certificates didn't match. Someone had used a middle, maiden or maternal last name, or hadn't officially recognized a child. Or the certificates were no longer legible. This was heartbreaking to kids and families. A dead end.

Candelaria had been sent to the U.S. after an earthquake swallowed half her home. They built a makeshift shelter and worked for the usual dollar-a-day on neighboring farms. Her first cousin in Arkansas paid her trip in order to help, but it took three months to locate all the birth certificates.

While waiting for those records, the rules changed. The federal government declared that minors going to any relative but a parent had to prove they were related AND provide photographs or phone records showing a personal relationship.

Candelaria lived in a mud and log shanty, half of which was at the bottom of a ravine.

Without photographs or phone company records, Candelaria became stranded. She used the months that followed to hone a skill in painting. She revealed that she played piano in an evangelical church, so we bought a small electric and put it in the rear counseling office. During our sessions, we would look up piano YouTubes and learn new songs. My clinical supervisor was an accomplished banda musician, and he would come in and teach Candelaria new Latin riffs. Painting, drawing and music kept her sane while she waited for a miracle: a photograph discovered, an offer of foster care, a return to the previous rules.

Toward the end of that week's session, I asked if she had any news from home.

"My grandmother died."

"I'm so sorry. When?"

"Yesterday. She was killed."

"Oye mija, what do you mean killed? Sit down."

She had spoken matter-of-factly, standing at the piano, getting ready to leave. She followed me to the office chairs by my computer.

"My mother told me on the phone today."

"This is horrible."

"Some people came into our house and cut her neck with a machete. They broke things too."

I paused a moment. Taking that in.

"Oh, that's . . ." I couldn't think of the right word. "Do they have any idea who?"

"I think they are the people who leave notes in our small corn field. They want us to leave. They are going to bury her tomorrow."

Her reaction was flat, only informative, an affect numbed of necessity, I assumed.

I was momentarily at a loss, and all I could think of was "Do you want to talk to your mother a little more?"

"Can I call?"

The program director had issued a warning that ORR was aware of counselors and case managers giving their clients phone calls beyond their allotted, ten-minute weekly call. Our clinical supervisor had been direct: all requests for additional calls had to be cleared, be urgent and conducted in Spanish or with a translator on the line.

"Yes, you can make a quick call. And if your older brother is there, I want to speak with him. I want to offer my sadness for what happened to your grandmother."

The first call went to a fake voice mail. That was a familiar glitch in the cell phone system of Guatemala. Kids told me the voice mail didn't exist. It was just a random message from the cell phone company.

"It's the rains right now. Sometimes calls can't get over the mountains," she said.

The third try gave us the long tones we needed.

A voice answered in Mam, Guatemala's major language. I had a tight, nervous stomach looking at the door. My boss would walk in and see my client on the phone, speaking in a language I didn't understand. And I couldn't blame him for being angry: they could be discussing anything. Escape plans for all I knew.

Kids did speak in their various Mayan languages during their scheduled weekly phone call. Those ten minutes gave homesick kids just enough time to ask about relatives and siblings, ask about their sponsor and get a pep talk from mom and dad. The phone room sounded a lot like the crying room at church.

But additional calls were another matter.

"Here's my brother," and she pointed to the speakerphone.

"Ranold?"

"Si, si Don Arturo."

"I'm so sorry about your grandmother. It's terrible. How are you and your parents?"

"Si, si. We must leave the house and go to my uncles. Bad people. Tomorrow we bury her."

I allowed Candelaria to say goodbye and asked if it would be hard for her to sleep tonight.

"Yes, I think I will have dreams."

Not eating and nightmares were behaviors that youth workers were required to report at the end of each shift.

I emailed my supervisors that a child reported a death. An assistant clinical director responded quickly and said I didn't have to file an official report. The child didn't see the murder, and it wasn't her parent. But we needed to let the other staff know in case of triggers, and we needed to place her on close observation.

The assistant didn't ask how I verified the death, although I think he knew.

On the walk down the stairs, I decided that next time I would have a translator on the line. This was foolish risk, and I liked this job.

Two

Every counselor was on a rotation for night watch. At eleven-thirty, my cell phone lit and vibrated my pillow. I picked up, and the shift leader from the boy's dormitory said that Lazaro was huddled in the closet and trembling.

He'd been in the shelter for eight months, failed by two sponsors but still with options.

"Call his mother and let her talk to him. If that doesn't work, I'll come right down."

A few minutes later, I received a callback. The shift leader said that when his mother answered, Lazaro wept and said in spurts, "The demon says I owe him because I haven't helped you, because I'm still here."

His mother listened and when he was done, she told him to settle down and ask for a video call. A minute later, the shift leader called her back through WhatsApp.

Seeing his mother's face quieted Lazaro, and they spoke calmly as she walked her cell phone to a small family altar. There, he watched her place food offerings that would satisfy the accusing spirit. She told Lazaro to stop worrying and behave himself.

I stayed up for an hour and then allowed myself to doze off.

The next morning, I documented the evening call and set out to check on both Candelaria and Lazaro. But it was Friday.

Every youth in the shelter attended the Friday celebration. Teachers gave awards to the most improved, best conduct, most supportive of peers. It was a big deal for students. Many had only minimal schooling, and this was a great validation. They made projects that went on display and signed up for performances: karaoke, rapping, dance and class skits. It was fun and made Fridays special.

Lazaro was on student council and giving a pep talk. In Guatemala, he had completed eighth grade, a rarity among farm children, and his uncle had taught him to play various musical instruments. School bands were important in Guatemala, and poor rural schools sacrificed to purchase instruments. This made Lazaro's expertise valuable, and from age fourteen he had been the music teacher for the local elementary school.

After the ceremony and in my office, Lazaro apologized for the evening call. He hadn't meant to wake me up.

Once talking, he shared that guilt had intensified over months of not helping his mother. His young siblings needed his income. I probed a bit around the idea that frustration and fear had triggered a dream or hallucination, but that idea made no sense to him. The specter had been real, and he explained in detail how and why it preyed on him. I expressed my admiration at his mother's ability to handle spiritual threats and bring him comfort.

"Anything else happening at home."

"My father. He's looking for me. He said if I don't send money, he's going to hurt my little sister."

"I thought he disappeared?"

"He was with this other family. He needs money, I think. That's when he reappears, not to help my mom."

"Would he hurt your sister?"

"He tried to kill me twice. The first time he was drunk, and the other he chased me with a gun because I couldn't find cement blocks. His bullets missed, so he beat my mother instead."

"The police didn't do anything?"

"They have no power. And he pays them. I have to get my mother and sister out of there."

"You have family, Lazaro—they need to help your mom. Right now, you can't."

He made small nods, seeming to agree.

"Are you afraid to go back?"

"He'll kill me if I don't return with money. My mom said the army changed him. He had to follow orders and shoot old people and families."

"When is your next call home?"

"Today."

"Okay, I'm going to check with you after the call. I have to report this. The lawyers need to know about your dad. This country doesn't send kids back to be killed."

I sent an email, and a few minutes later, my supervisor came in with a youth worker to escort Lazaro to his classroom. The case manager joined us with her own director. Everyone had been pulled from some other task. We staffed everything: the previous night's occurrence, the phone call to his mother, the father's previous attempts to kill Lazaro and the current threat.

"We definitely file a Serious Incident Report," said my supervisor. "Does he have a sponsor?"

"Maybe a new one," replied the case manager. "His sponsor keeps lying about sending documents. He just failed again, and we waited three weeks."

"He has an older sister in Oklahoma," I said.

"Leave that to the case managers. That's not your job," replied my supervisor. "We've talked about this before. Same for the lawyers. That has to come from Lazaro."

The lawyers came every week and once a month talked to every minor in the shelter. The sessions were short. Did the child have a sponsor? If yes, that ended the session.

If not, it depended on the lawyer what happened next. They worked for a non-profit that received government funding, and depending on the political environment, they could be very helpful.

The law said it was up to each minor to share what they wanted with the lawyers, but the children did not have to share their legal proceedings with counselors or case managers. Technically, we weren't even allowed to ask.

But being human, most of us did.

I walked down to the phone room with my laptop and wrote my Serious Incident Report while waiting for Lazaro to get his turn. These "SIR's" went to everyone in the chain of command, at both the shelter and Homeland Security.

After Lazaro finished his call, we met for a few minutes in an empty nursing room.

"My family is staying with my aunt. It's crowded, but she has to."

"Lazaro, I met with my supervisors, and I sent a report to the government about your father. When you meet with the lawyers next week, you absolutely must tell them everything you told me. All the details."

"But I don't need them. I have my uncle."

"I don't know what's wrong with your uncle, but he keeps lying. He hasn't sent us a single document."

"What about my sister?"

"Maybe, but you know it takes time. You need to tell the lawyers you don't have a sponsor and that your father will kill you. The court won't send a kid back to die."

"Can I do both? I want to go with my sister."

"Yes, do both. I know you don't want a group home. But you need a sure thing."

"So, I don't have a sponsor?"

"Your case manager wasted a lot of time with him. She'll talk to you, but you need to get the lawyers involved."

Three

With the day running short, I decided to take my new clients straight from the dining room. We were not allowed to interrupt meals, but with new arrivals, they could bring dinner trays to the office. I called out for Edison Tzep and a lanky, serious faced boy stood up. Once up the five floors and in the office, I opened my laptop to both Google Earth and the ORR's secure website.

"You're fifteen-years-old, Edison?"

"No, I'm sixteen."

"But you were born on this year, and I pointed to the screen."

"Yes, I think so. I'm sixteen."

I remembered that for Guatemalans after your first birthday, you were considered in the second year of life. You were two years old.

"In the U.S. we count differently. We say you're still one during your second year."

The boy didn't respond.

"You get to be fifteen again. A free extra year."

That got a puzzled smile.

I asked about daily life, and he answered that his family farm produced enough corn to eat for eight months. They supplemented their income by harvesting cardamom and coffee.

"How much do you earn?"

"Two dollars for the day, when there is work."

"I hear cardamom is dangerous because of snakes."

"My cousin died from a bite. You don't see them."

I asked how they managed on so little, and he said his mother made a thick, corn tortilla in the evening, and that was usually their meal. If there wasn't enough for his younger siblings, then he would eat less or not at all that day. The same for his dog, he told me.

I finished with Edison, and quickly retrieved the next new intake. Yovani was seventeen and lived on a mountainside facing one of Guatemala's great and active volcanoes. He made extra money walking travelers up and down the Atitlan, and he had purchased a used camera with that money.

I took a few minutes to explore what might be possible in the U.S. I googled the high school he would likely attend, and we watched a slick school YouTube produced by the student film club. His sponsoring aunt lived in a state where undocumented students paid normal college tuition, so we scanned for photography classes at the junior college. He said he would like to be a wedding photographer, and I showed him a site that listed typical fees charged by U.S. photographers. He translated dollars to Guatemalan quetzales: one wedding shoot would earn him an income equal to fifteen years of farming back home.

In rural Guatemala, photography was a big luxury, and he had been criticized for spending his earnings on it. It's why he wanted to be in the U.S. Back home, he would ever only be a poor farmer who led tourists up and down a volcano.

Yovani asked me if he would be a legal person when he left the shelter. This was a common question, and I explained that he would be in the asylum process, and during that time, he was supposed to be in school and not work.

That was the official answer to this question. But these kids didn't brave all manner of difficulty to then sit on their hands while parents and siblings starved and struggled. Some case managers and counselors stayed to the safer answer: the law says you must be in school and not work. Make sure you stay in school.

Others, like myself, acknowledged more of the practical reality. They had to go to school, and they needed to work. I let Yovani know he would be working illegally, and I could not offer any advice in that regard. But I was happy to discuss jobs, trades, education and help him see the opportunities, avoid the difficulties, and envision a life in America.

I asked Yovani a question that had been bothering me. My own family farmed in Mexico. I knew the economics of poor farmers. I went back to Google Earth and zoomed in over the farms of his region.

"Where are the animals? How do you plow?"

"Señor Arturo, how would you get them up the mountain. And they eat too much."

Duh. These were terraced farms, slanted farms, and mostly small family plots broken up between other people's strips of land.

"So, you can't use animals or machines?"

"No one can afford them. And they wouldn't help much."

"You plant like your Mayan ancestors, everything by hand."

"That's what they tell us in school."

Rosalinda had arrived the day before. Her case manager said I could not interrupt her church service as he pointed her out in the cafeteria: the tallest of three girls standing in front of an older woman with rosary beads and a prayer book. The lady had been sent by the local Catholic Church to hand out communion. The three girls wore veils borrowed from our clothing room. My client's embroidered, white veil, dark profile and modest dress gave me an immediate sense of Guadalupe, the Mexican Madonna. The service took place in a corner of the dining room, sharing that space with cooks, youth workers and kids busy on projects and board games.

At our delayed first session, I told Rosalinda I hadn't wanted to interrupt the communion service, but now we were within minutes of the twenty-four hours permitted. We would have to move quickly through the intake.

Rosalinda displayed the courtesy common to her peers, but unlike them, she looked me in the eye when she spoke, with a steady voice and posture. I entered the information about her journey, who paid for it, her school and work history. She was from a *municipio*, a rural town that served as the capital of a district. She farmed and cooked in a small restaurant. Until recently, she had been in school, and I asked why she left.

"I am a lesbian woman, that's why I'm here. A gang at school told me not to come back anymore. Cars followed me and made threats. Then they started calling my mother on her cell phone."

"What were the threats?"

"They were going to burn our house."

"Did you think the threats were real?"

"They tried. They shot into the house and threw a lit bottle. We were lucky no one was home and our neighbors put out the fire."

"And this is because they know you're lesbian?

"Yes, that's what they say. Maybe they also want to take our house. I don't know, but I never came home after they shot the door. I went to my aunt's house and left from there."

"You'll be safe here in the shelter. And in this country, you can be yourself. That's one of the best things about the United States."

"I know. That's why I'm here."

Eberr Tut was my last intake. He fled Guatemala after several beatings on the mountain path from school to his farm. These were thieves and gang members from El Salvador who had moved into Guatemala and were preying on villages. This particular gang hid in the woods that lined the only road into the nearest town. Eberr told me some of the villages in Guatemala were fighting back, but his own was doing nothing.

Aside from beatings when they found him on the forest path, the gang members stripped him of anything valuable. He couldn't go to school anymore or shop for his mother. His parents sent him away because he was their only son, and the most likely to be killed.

"What about your father?"

"He works far and only comes home on the weekend. He sleeps outside with the other workers and doesn't have a phone."

"So, what's going to happen to your mother and sisters?"

"They have to walk around the mountain now. It takes two hours to the town, but it's safe. When I start working, I'll send money so they can stay in a house on the river Chixoy, and my sisters can go back to school."

I asked his age and he replied, "Maybe fifteen." He didn't know his birth date. I then asked about his siblings and his answer was the same: *I don't know.*

"Eberr, you can't answer 'I don't know' to these questions. Not in this country."

Guatemalan children were usually soft spoken and taciturn. From their seventh year, they spent their days planting and harvesting crops. They worked hard, lived lean and did not possess the chatty habits of their American peers. They seldom questioned an adult, but Eberr appeared tired and annoyed.

"Age doesn't matter, mister. We never talk about it."

I knew from my other clients that many poor families did not celebrate or acknowledge birthdays. It hit me that time itself did not matter; not when you worked from childhood and nothing ever changed.

"I know that in Guatemala age and birthdays are not that important. You grow up fast in your country. But in the United States you are still a child. You're not even old enough work."

"But everyone works."

"Not here. Everything is about age in this country, and it's very strict. That's why if you say you don't know how old your sister is, people will be surprised. They might think something is wrong with you, or worse, that you are hiding something. People in the United States keep track of everything. Everything is in a computer, and they expect you to know your birthday and everything about your family.

We went through the siblings and their ages again and he thought harder. What he didn't know, he tried to approximate. *Yes, I think she's young. Maybe she's twenty-five.*

Four

All of us worked either Saturday or Sunday. No employee had a full weekend off. Someone had to watch the kids.

For the children, the weekends were about special activities, field trips and chores.

I arrived at eight in the morning, and all three dormitory floors were busy with buckets and brooms, mops, sponges, Pine-Sol and bleach. Like children everywhere, our minors were expected to clean their rooms. Each bedroom elected a task leader to supervise the routine: sweep and mop the room and hallway, change bedding, scrub the tub, sink and toilet. They didn't need prodding and seemed to enjoy doing something practical.

At nine, I walked down to the girl's wing and looked for Dayeli. I had observed her in class during the week, and I noticed that if the other girls raised their hands, so did she. Every time. I had no idea how she processed what was occurring, but she displayed the common teenage desire to feel included and not singled out. Her teacher emailed that Dayeli was learning how to write her name, and for now she was to copy the work of her deskmate.

That seemed a logical start.

My session with Dayeli was brief. I had printed a set of pictures to ask if she felt comfortable in the classroom and with other teens, if she liked our food, and if she felt safe in the shelter. I took a minute on the Internet to zoom in on an aerial view of her Guatemalan home, and I showed her a video someone posted of her village. Her eyes lit as she pointed to the screen and herself. I gave her a blank page and pencil, and with a slow, concentrated effort she wrote her name. I gave her a thumbs-up.

When I pointed to the broom in our office, she nodded yes. She wanted to end the session and get back to her friends and chores.

Up on the fourth floor I found Henry Ixcoy. After nearly a year, he was in the top tier of long-term residents. They were a small, suffering group, and at every meeting they used their seniority to give motivational speeches about patience, faith in God and how to use time in the shelter to prepare for what would come after.

Henry was leaving that day. Minors always arrived at night and left at night. His flight was set to leave the next morning at six. Today would be all about goodbyes.

Outside of a fist bump, no touching was allowed in the shelter. Not between clients or between workers and clients. I would have enjoyed giving Henry a hug goodbye, but a final handshake was already pushing it.

Henry's aunt was president of the congress of Mayan languages, and he could speak both Mam and Ixil. He had been raised by his mother, but dad regularly sent money and called his son from Oregon. At sixteen, he had waited a lifetime to see his father in person. When he first arrived one year ago, his case manager had him ready for exit within the normal fourteen-day parent transfer.

His father had already paid for a flight through the approved travel agency. Because Henry was over thirteen, his father did not have to purchase the additional chaperon ticket. The father was on the phone reviewing exit arrangements with a case manager when he said, "I'm glad they have a late flight because we have court in the morning."

The case manager stopped everything. Apparently, a fight between Henry's dad and stepmom resulted in a visit from the police. Dad and Stepmom took a plea of disturbing the peace, but the judge said they would have to attend counseling sessions, or the charge would become domestic violence. The whole process dragged on for months. Since courts were involved, the father's status with immigration was put on hold, and we could not release the child to a sponsor whose legal immigration status was in review.

Henry cried and sulked and alternated between anger and disbelief. During the weeks that followed, he asked to see us constantly and heard the same news he'd heard earlier. Eventually, he assimilated the situation and began to see himself as necessary to the shelter. He helped other kids acclimate, took extra chores and became obsessed with mastering English, student leadership and winning chess tournaments. He celebrated his sixteenth birthday in the cafeteria and waltzed in a group *quinceañera* improvised for several Catholic girls in the shelter. In the end,

Henry accepted release to an uncle in Oregon, a couple hundred miles from Dad.

My session with Ilso was also connected to leaving. We had scheduled an important call to his parents, and while we waited for his case manager to join us, thirteen-year-old Ilso asked if he could watch a YouTube. It was in his Popti language and made by some funny guys from Jakaltenango.

Knowing that he lived in a thatch roof shack without power or plumbing, and that from the pictures I'd seen of his region, this was common, I was surprised by the production quality of the video. Two guys were dressed in Mayan village drag—in this case wigs and the traditional woven skirts of Jakaltenango women. The guys acted out a scene where one washed clothing at the river while the other milled corn for tortillas. Then a lost young man surprised them. What followed were silly antics not too different from what my Tik-Tok addicted, tween daughters find hilarious.

We then listened to a Popti pop singer, and Ilso, who was a wiry, five feet and all mischief, softly sang along. He had a high, little boy voice, and he placed his head near the screen to sing.

"How do you watch videos without electricity?"

"The government gave everyone a solar panel and a battery that we paid for with corn."

"How big a panel?"

Ilso stretched his arms about three feet.

"And you can watch YouTubes with it?"

"It charges a cell phone, and we have a light bulb now. My dad turns it on so I can do homework."

"How did you do it before?"

"Candles, but they cost money and made my eyes hurt."

Like many kids in the shelter, they were trapped by new federal regulations. His first and second sponsors backed out when told that everyone in the household, including roommates, would have to be fingerprinted by police. This was a new requirement and his relatives didn't even want to ask. It was an impossible request, they said. But a new option had emerged.

The case manager joined us, and with a Popti translator listening, we made the call to his family.

Ilso and his parents spoke about family, village friends and he gently queried his six-year-old sister about her chores and chickens. She had been very attached to Ilso, and he missed her the most. Then he asked, "Mama, should I stay here. What if I want to come home?"

"Mijo, you can always come home. You know that. But you know how we live. It's up to you."

"They say I can live in a house with a family, and I can have my own room and work when I'm fifteen. They said I can call you every day."

Ilso started to cry, and his mother with him. Then she asked if he wanted to go to school and have a future and help his sister someday. As the crying stopped and the conversation became sober, Ilso turned around to ask us "Can I have a television in my room?"

The case manager, who had spent so much time speaking with his family that she felt like a surrogate aunt said, "Yes, you'll have a television and Internet. And a phone to call your mom. As long as you go to school and behave."

Ilso receded into his thoughts, but his expression suggested he had made up his mind.

On the walk back from dropping Ilso on the soccer field, one of the recreation leaders called me over.

"I need to tell you something. It's your new client, Yasly. He talks to himself and says crazy things. I was working night shift when they brought him in, and he told us he knew how to fly. He's been talking to himself in class, and the other students are avoiding him."

That scared me. I was off the day of his intake, and I hadn't reviewed the session notes. It was probably all there.

"Give me two hours and I'll come for him. If anything comes up just call on the radio and I'll come right down."

I proceeded to see my next two clients. Both were bright, ambitious kids, but they would be attending nearly all white rural schools upon release. We explored how this might be difficult: it would be easy to feel intimidated and tempting to drop out and just work on a farm. Both teens noted the absence of Hispanic students in club videos from the high school. I emphasized that in the U.S. a high school diploma and fluent English were as expected as a third-grade education was in Guatemala. They said the high school looked like a university, but the students seemed so informal. It was all odd to them, but they assured me it was more exciting than frightening.

It was three in the afternoon. I had my own children to pick up in two hours.

In the dining room, the youth worker pointed out Yasly to me.

He was chewing slowly, maintaining a blank expression as two of his peers gave their farewell talks. He was fixated on something in the distance. When his table was finally excused, I met him at the trashcans where trays were emptied, introduced myself as his regular counselor and asked him to come with me.

In the office he told me that he came alone on a bus, all the way from Honduras. His mother lived in Texas. She left when he was six and he missed her, and his grandparents were getting to old to take care of him.

Except for his wandering gaze, everything seemed fine. I asked about life on his grandparents' farm, and he said it had been fun. There was a grove of trees and using ropes, he had often swung from one end of the forest to the other. He had also survived a drop over a great waterfall. And while jaguars were rare and endangered, one lived in a tree near his home, but he said nothing to his family about it.

I emailed my supervisor as well as the dormitory staff: there was some concern about Yasly, and he would be on close observation for the next few days.

At nine p.m. I received the call. Yasly was actively hallucinating and threatening to fly through a window. I asked them to call the city's psychological crisis unit—always the first step—while I drove my daughters to their mother's house.

I arrived with the crisis unit already there, and they began their interview. After a few questions, their lead, a former pro boxer from South Boston asked me, "Does he look at everyone that way, or does it seem he's got something with me?"

The crisis unit drove him to the nearest child psychiatric unit that had a bed. One of the youth workers on night shift accompanied Yasly and I followed. I waited a few hours until he was signed in and had a bed. The youth worker stayed in the room till morning. The shelter always provided bedside staff when our children were hospitalized.

Five

The next morning, the case manager and I had a long conversation with Yasly's mother. Part of the reason she initially came to the U.S. was to pay for his medical bills. He had been a preemie and often hospitalized as a young child. The health issues subsided, but he went occasionally to a therapist in the city and had been prescribed medication. She sent money for all of this, but his grandparents had become too frail to take him into town and keep up.

I visited Yasly at the hospital, and as before, he was in story-telling mode. But he knew where he was, and who he was. At the shelter, we began a process to get him into treatment and on medication. Any psychological testing or hospitalization involved calls, forms and emails to various directors. Once everyone had agreed to the need, we began the second flurry of calls to find a bed in a treatment facility. We wanted Yasly delivered directly from the hospital.

On the morning he was released from the hospital, his case manager and I drove him to a treatment center. I didn't like the feel of it. Cold, white walled and sterile. The intake nurse kept speaking to him in English, asking questions and smiling, even though she knew he didn't understand a word of it. But we had no choice. They had a translation machine that would allow him to participate in group sessions, and the psychiatrist would see him every other day.

I visited on the fourth day, and apparently the treatment staff knew what they were doing. He was on a low dose medication that impeded hallucination, and he appeared happy and a bit more centered. He had a couple stories to tell about the facility, but they were plausible.

One week later we had him back, much better, medication having kicked in, and he did well the next few days. He still told tall tales: his teacher reported that Yasly said to the entire class that he could not sleep at night because if his foot stuck out the blanket, an old woman descended and kissed his toe.

I was convinced these stories were a different issue from the hallucinations. Just a habit, a personality quirk, a compensation for a difficult childhood. I considered that he was fine to travel. The next step was finding a treatment center near his mother's home and have them agree to monitor his medication and provide therapy. With only one clinic not on a wait list, ten of us huddled around a speaker phone, with agency directors listening, and we made our best pitch for continued treatment.

It worked, they agreed. It was a fifteen-minute bus ride. Yasly and his mom would be okay, and we could now put Yasly on a plane to Dallas.

Except we couldn't. Both ORR and our own agency psychologist said he needed to be cleared by a psychiatrist for flight. There was no way to board him without a medical clearance.

Ah, that was a problem. There were only two psychiatrists in the city that would see our kids. After much pleading, one of them made room for an evaluation. We would translate as she only spoke English.

The youth worker who came with us was an older gentleman. A pleasant, formal man named Patricio who bore a striking similarity to the handsome "I don't always drink beer" actor. He liked Yasly, and we had a pleasant drive to the office. Along the way, Patricio told him, "If you want to fly on an airplane, you can't tell your stories. They'll think you're crazy. No ghosts or Tarzan—understand, Yasly."

Yasly nodded quietly. As we exited the car, I said, "Patricio is right. Your mom is waiting for you. This doctor doesn't know you. Think about what you say."

The psychiatrist was experienced, had dealt often with our clients, and operated from a deep core of calm and common sense. She began to ask questions that both Patricio and I translated. She complimented Yasly and made him comfortable. All was going well until she asked, "Have unusual or extraordinary things ever happened to you."

I was seated next to Yasly, and Patricio was on the couch to my left. I saw Yasly's eyes light up and knew exactly what would follow his blooming grin.

Patricio dropped his water bottle, excused himself, and stretched to retrieve it. He shot Yasly a quick but loud gaze, accentuated by the arch of his bushy, white brows.

The psychiatrist asked again, "Has anything unusual or extraordinary ever happened to you?"

Yasly stared at the floor, shook two fingers and nodded his head back and forth, doing all he could, I assumed, to keep back a whopper.

Six

It was after lunch and I was looking forward to my next session. Anup was one of three boys from India in the shelter. Our first session had been conducted with a human translator on speakerphone. After that, we managed with Google translator.

In our shelters, approximately eighty percent of the unaccompanied minors arrived from Guatemala. Another fifteen percent from Honduras and El Salvador. The remaining five percent came to us from small pockets of violent terrain in Mexico and India.

Children from Mexico were turned back at the border unless they came from specific provinces known for Cartel violence, and they had to bear tangible proof of threat. It was rare, but when they were allowed passage into the U.S., their stories were tragic and terrifying. The kids from India were also of a type. They didn't speak English, and they were fleeing rural, politically difficult regions. They never told us the whole truth about their journey. But the trip from India was expensive, so there had to be a very real fear behind it.

Anup's story was that he fled the village after joining a political party, and an important man paid for his plane ticket after seeing him beat-up by political thugs. According to Anup, the plane landed in Ecuador, and then he begged his way to the U.S., walking and hitching rides most of the way.

Of course, that was impossible. There's a place called Panama between here and Ecuador, and he would have trekked through jungle. And he knew no Spanish upon arriving at our shelter. More likely, he landed in Mexico and was driven to the U.S. border where he turned himself in and asked for asylum. His family in India checked out fine, and there was no point in arguing about his travels. Anup walked from Ecuador and that was that.

The other constant about kids from India is that they always had an uncle in the U.S. that turned out to be a very good family friend, but not an uncle. In India, a close family friend was a relative for all practical purposes. Same true in lots of places. But for U.S. immigration, not even close. An uncle had to be blood.

This was hard for Anup to understand. After many discussions, I finally sat him down with the case manager and told him, "You're going to be here until your eighteen. That is eight months from now."

"But, but, my uncle."

"No uncle, Anup. This is settled. You leave at eighteen. Unless you have a blood relative, and you don't, that's the deal." The case manager volleyed the same concise message to him.

Anup cried, and he cried some more.

And then he stopped, raised his head, stood up his six-foot frame, slapped the desk and said, "I adapt!"

That changed everything. We explained what would happen the day he turned eighteen. He would be an adult, so no need for a sponsor. Since he had a case pending with immigration, he would be released to the nearest bus station. The non-profit lawyers would arrange for his family friend to send a bus ticket, and he would have to approach the ticket window to retrieve it. We would get him ready for that day but could not go with him. It would be scary, but so far no one had been lost.

He should also ask his uncle to please buy a card with forty dollars on it and mail it to the lawyers in his name. Otherwise, it would be a very hungry ride from one side of the country to the other.

During the six months that followed that conversation, Anup learned not only basic English, but was near fluent in Spanish and could count in Qanhobal, the language of his roommates. During counseling sessions, we sometimes downloaded Indian pop songs from the Internet while investigating the town he would be moving too. We spent months discussing recreation, dating in the U.S., schools, businesses, music—all the interests of any young man.

Isidro gave Anup a fist bump as I dropped off one client to retrieve the other. Isidro was a kind, handsome, and articulate young man. The kind you'd like for your daughter. He immediately took leadership in the shelter, and he made it a point to welcome the Hindu boys. He and Anup had become good friends, communicating through hand signals, bits of English, and lately in Spanish.

"You should have seen us at the dance," said Isidro. "The DJ put on one of his India songs. Most of the boys are shy.

The boys from Honduras and El Salvador always dance, but the Guatemalans mostly watch.

"All the girls dance," I said. "I see the big line."

"Of course," said Isidro. "But when the DJ played an Anup song, no one knew what to do. Anup was in the middle of the cafeteria by himself and started waving his arms and hips around. I ran over and did what he did."

Isidro stood up from his chair, and with a big smile displayed his new Indian arm and hip maneuvers.

"When they saw me, my friends got brave and started dancing with us, too."

Again, he did his best Indian pop moves. I imagined the end of a Bollywood wedding movie.

Seven

Shelters are not prisons. I was watching from my office when a Honduran teen kicked the soccer ball over the classrooms and bolted over the wall. Lanky and tall, he had worked in the Salinas lettuce fields before risking a trip home when his mother was hospitalized. To get back after she recovered, and to pay her medical bills, he rode the migrant trains to Tijuana, and then walked two days to San Luis. There he propped a ladder onto the border fence and jumped over, landing on top of a clothing store. The roof gave and a fitting room broke his fall. Border Patrol agents saw him jump over the fence, and if not for a sales lady who hid him, would have cornered him in the store.

He felt lucky and blessed. Brayan found work that same day climbing palm trees to shake dates off the branches. A co-worker rented him a bit of floor space to lay a mat, and Brayan started saving. He knew it was safest to pay a coyote to smuggle him from Yuma to central California since there would be ICE checkpoints. But he soon had enough for a bus ticket and ignored his better judgement. He boarded a Greyhound bus in Yuma and headed to the lettuce and strawberry fields of Salinas.

Border Patrol agents boarded his bus at the California line. A few days later, he arrived at our shelter.

The day he scaled our wall, two other boys followed him. One jumped and one stopped short. The one who hesitated said he knew immediately he shouldn't have joined. He would now pay for that by being sent to a secure, escape-proof shelter, but he was fine with that: the boys who jumped knew where they were going. He didn't.

That was our only escape for the year. After that incident, the wall was fortified with netting, and youth workers stationed at vulnerable points. We were not allowed to tackle or restrain kids, even if they were running. We were not allowed to touch any of the minors in the shelter; and even in self-defense, we had to use the least-violent response. All staff received frequent training in defensive measures that did not require striking a youth. If a kid was simply running away, with no clear peril to his or her safety, all we could do was make it difficult.

Isidro told me that during the last fire drill, when all the minors were taken to the parking lot and surrounded by the entire staff, his heart was racing. He knew we couldn't physically restrain him, and he could easily get past us and over the concrete block.

So why didn't he run? Why didn't other kids run?

The lesser reason was that all of us were trained to notice signs of escape interest: kids who looked at the wall or asked questions about the other side. Kids who appeared to be faking illness for doctor visits. Any minor who mentioned anything related to escape or survival afterward. These events were immediately reported, and the young person was categorized as a run-risk. Included were children who lost a sponsor or were approaching eighteen without a sponsor. And once a minor appeared on the run-list, field trips were prohibited, close observation required, and they were placed in classrooms inside the building. They hated it. Sometimes they were put on the list without merit, and this was difficult. But in general, fear of being listed kept kids on their best behavior.

The more powerful restraint was the child's awareness that the consequences would be disastrous. This wasn't Mexico where it was easy to hitch rides, find work and a place to shelter. Here they would be lost in an unknown city, without money or a phone, without food or a place to sleep. They would be looked for. The police would investigate if they were found sleeping in alleyways. They had no family near the shelter, so no one would come for them. And being caught by border patrol or police would result in a quick deportation. Kids preferred to stay in the shelter, pray and hope.

I ended the day talking with Edvin Xiloj, a cheery, small sixteen-year-old with endless optimism. He spoke Spanish with a choppy accent, and his sentences kept to the matter-of-fact statements common to children from the countryside. He smiled continuously.

We discussed the afternoon's excitement and what everyone was saying about the escape. Edvin said that Brayan had been hard to catch in soccer, and that's why he always covered him.

"You must be fast. Brayan was in good shape."

"I'm the fastest in my state."

"You're a runner?"

"No. I just worked on the farm with my brothers. But one day I heard about a race."

"What kind?"

"The race around the whole city. There is a prize for the fastest and everyone wants to win."

"Had you ever been in a race?"

"No. Only in school. But I heard about it and I knew I could win. I told my father that I had to run and asked for the entry money. He said, 'You're not a runner,' and I said, 'But I can win.'"

I had heard from other kids about these municipal races. They were important in Guatemala.

"The next day, I went to the city and paid thirty quetzales. Runners from all the villages started together, but I saw only one boy with me at the end, and I ran faster. I came home and told my father that I won the first prize."

"I imagine he was surprised. What did he say?"

"He said that it was good I won the prize."

From his first day, Edvin displayed no sign of anxiety. He never asked when he was leaving, never acted out. He had nothing but good things to say about his days in the shelter and the people around him.

"Edvin," I said. "You're one of the few kids I never worry about. You never complain or cry, you never lose hope."

"Mister, why would I lose hope? That would make me sad. I didn't come into this world to suffer."

Eight

About kids in cages.

It might take as few as five days on a bus to get from Guatemala to the U.S. border, but for most minors it took weeks and months. The latter group made their way slowly, working on farms and cleaning homes to continue their journey. They often hid in villages or towns for weeks if they knew Mexican immigration was canvassing the area. But whether it had been a fast, fortunate and expensive bus ride or weeks on the road, there were three choices once they arrived at the border

Many braved a large Mexican city and found their way to the U.S. border station. They stood in line and once in front of the agent, a few feet into the United States, they gave their name and asked for asylum. Another large group did the opposite and tried to stay away from the city. Instead, they walked along the border into the desert. At some point, they scaled the fence. In areas with tall, modern fencing, the guides provided ladders and rope, and we sometimes received kids with fall injuries. Once on the U.S. side, they walked to the nearest road, and there they waited for immigration agents to pick them up.

And then a very small group, maybe five percent, scaled the fence with the intent of walking through the desert. The guides, or coyotes, rarely accompanied them. The desert was dangerous, and Border Patrol had cameras, motion sensors, aircraft, horse patrols and all-terrain vehicles. They were going to get caught, and for a coyote that meant jail time. The guides didn't chance it.

Instead, kids received directions to follow along mountains and walk toward landmarks. They were told to take all the water they could carry. The destination was usually a farmhouse or rural road where someone should be waiting. The wandering minors were usually caught within the first day or two. Those who managed to walk further told us horrifying stories of leaving people to die, finding human remains, hallucinating, and being wounded by snakes and cactus. Many kids were found because they flagged aircraft from an open space, hoping immigration would find them before they succumbed. The Southwest desert was for all intents impassable except with great luck or by great expense.

But regardless of how a minor was detained—asking for asylum at the border, waiting by a roadside or found trekking through the desert—what happened next was uniform. Border agents drove their charges to nearby detention facilities, small jails dotting the ocean to ocean border. There, the unaccompanied minors spent two or three days in uncomfortable but bearable conditions. The kids called it the *Yelera,* or freezer, because of the concrete floors and unheated cells. They had mats and packaged food. It could get crowded, the guards might be mean, and they were pressured to request voluntary repatriation. Kids found it scary and uncomfortable, but they had endured worse and it was over quickly. They had more to fear from the police of their own countries.

After necessary processing, and sometimes the same day, the minors were put in a van and delivered to an appropriate shelter

There were seasonal patterns: children came after the harvest, when weather permitted, when the school year ended.

The shelters were elastic. They could accommodate one hundred or five hundred clients. Previous administrations had always pressed the whole system to be efficient and safe, and for children to spend as little time as possible in the barren jails along the border. They wanted kids moved quickly to safe and highly regulated youth shelters. In part, this stemmed from the Flores court case, but at the end of the day, Americans have a common antipathy to injustice and cruelty, and always where children are concerned.

During my second year at the shelter, Washington decided on a new tack to impede the flow of unaccompanied minors. The Federal government could not easily change asylum laws, but they could inject a good dose of pain, fear and loss into the process.

The government knew that the relatives waiting to sponsor were commonly undocumented and low-wage workers. They seldom had the means to rent a house or apartment by themselves, and most lived in a large, extended family or with unrelated roommates. Under previous rules, only the sponsor had to be fingerprinted and undergo a complete background check. The housemates or extended family had only to provide an official ID, usually from their home country. That was enough for a basic criminal background check.

For an undocumented uncle or aunt, getting fingerprinted by police was frightening and risky, but they rarely said no. We could truthfully assure them the check was not for immigration, but to check for crimes. Likewise, housemates were usually willing to provide a copy of their ID. In worst case scenarios, a sponsor moved or found more amenable roommates. If there was any reason for concern, shelters had social workers available to visit the receiving home, inspect it and speak to all who lived there. The process had been in place for decades, and it worked to release kids efficiently and safety.

There was panic in the shelters when we received Washington's new regulation.

From now on, ALL members of a sponsor's household had to be fingerprinted by police in order to release a youth. Everyone. Homeland Security understood that while a child's sponsor would risk fingerprinting, the other adults in the house would balk. If only one adult in a home refused fingerprinting, the child stayed in the shelter.

The government's gambit worked: Instead of thirty days, kids now became stranded for months, without any idea if they would ever be released to family.

With our shelter filled to capacity as minors arrived but didn't leave, we had to convert every available space to a bedroom or classroom, and this meant we lost space, staff and time for the arts, music, field trips, exercise and recreation. Keeping hundreds of increasingly hopeless teens sane, occupied and safe became difficult and perilous. The government's rule change was meant to be punitive, to frustrate minors seeking asylum, frustrate their families and sponsors, and to pressure the network of shelters and organizations that helped these kids. It was a clear message that minors seeking asylum would experience long, uncertain waits in crowded, difficult conditions.

The government's campaign created a second nightmare at the border. With all shelters full, Border Patrol had nowhere to send unaccompanied minors. Their own detention facilities were small, bare and meant for quick turnover.

And that is how we got to kids in cages.

Immigration officials were forced to respond to bottleneck by improvising new shelters built in warehouses and military bases. Border Patrol was forced to hold kids in substandard detention much longer than was humane.

And this was before they started separating toddlers and five-year-olds from their parents.

Nine

Andrea Tzep arrived at our shelter traveling with two young siblings. She farmed potatoes on the coast of Guatemala, working on a small plot her father inherited, and she harvested corn on her mother's farm near Chixmaya. They grew enough to eat though not to sell, and this didn't leave money to attend school, which was free, but the books, pencils and exams cost money. To add income, Andrea ventured over the Mexican border to Tapachula, where Guatemalan girls were prized as inexpensive, live-in maids.

She arrived at a plaza where wealthier households looked for Guatemalan girls and accepted an offer of employment. Six months later, she returned to Chixmaya with enough money to pay for her siblings' school supplies, and she upgraded the family's sleeping mats to small beds.

After the harvest, she returned to Tapachula and this time contracted with another household. She was given a room, told she would eat with the family, get Sunday afternoons off and a fair, fixed salary. The first week, she was paid and treated as promised.

Her employers had an exporting business to California and traveled frequently. When they left, she looked after a toddler and seven-year-old. The couple appeared affluent, so she trusted when they said they were waiting for checks to clear. She didn't protest when she lost her day off in order to watch the children.

Then she was prohibited from using her cell phone or speaking to neighbors. When she complained, Andrea was informed that if she tried to run, she would not make it far. She was given a beating as a down payment on that threat.

Andrea explained that for three months she continued serving the household, hatching plots to escape but feeling that somehow, she had been stupid and brought this upon herself.

She paused her story to calm a tremor in her voice.

"I'm very strong, Don Arturo, but I didn't fight. I don't know why I was so afraid."

It wasn't until a relative working in Tapachula made multiple visits to the Federal police that hope returned. Andrea's employer was well known in Tapachula and the police paid a visit.

The couple denied having a maid or knowing anything about Andrea, but as soon as the police left, they called Andrea to the front door. The mother stuffed a handful of pesos into Andrea's hand and pushed her into the street, yelling, "You can't claim you weren't paid!"

The money was only a portion of what she was owed, but it was enough to get home, pack up her siblings, bundle some food, cross back into Mexico and pay for three bus tickets to the U.S. border.

On the first leg of their journey, Mexican immigration officials stopped the bus to check for Central American migrants. A woman from Mexico riding with her daughter told Andrea, "All of you sit with me, and put the little ones under my blanket. I'll say you're my children."

That was enough to get them to Puebla, and past patrols the U.S. had pressured Mexico to deploy at its southern border. But after that incident, she didn't trust the long-distance buses. She and her siblings took weeks hopping town-to-town on local buses and pickup trucks. She traded farm labor and housework for food and bedding.

I complemented Andrea on her tenacity and physical endurance, and she replied that she had grown up working and climbing mountains.

"Our family is the last Catholic clan in the village. We live closer to Chixmaya, but the church is near Senahu. My mother wakes us at four in the morning, and we walk five hours. Thirty of us, all my cousins, aunts and uncles, every Sunday. We stay in town and buy candy and then walk back before it gets dark. The trail is through forest and there are snakes and thieves, but we're safe in a big group."

She stated that she enjoyed being old-fashioned, although most girls weren't anymore, and she liked wearing the traditional Mayan *huipil* and *corte* of her region. She also knew how to use a loom and weave her own clothing. In counseling sessions, we looked to the Internet for what price indigenous dresses would fetch in the U.S., and I planted the idea that she might have a business with this skill.

Andrea's first sponsor got her in trouble. When a first cousin could not find photos to prove they had known each other in Guatemala, a clever friend used Photoshop to place Andrea into a picture with the sponsoring cousin. At first glance it looked good, at least to me. Our IT guy immediately spotted the fake, and her cousin was removed from consideration. But this was a bit of a blessing. In the months that followed, an aunt who earlier could not sponsor because of a legal residency process, now became eligible. In the meantime, Andrea attained a decent level of English and learned about websites like Etsy where she might sell her dresses.

For us at the shelter, Andrea became an asset, a girl with a calming influence on the young children who arrived one evening without warning.

Ten

Arnulfo Elias became one of my favorite kids. He was funny, eternally patient, and perfectly willing to bid his time until something worked out for him. He was our best soccer player, keeping us at the top of the shelter league, handsome but careful not to get tangled in gossip, and he reminded me every so often that he was not a run risk, and I wasn't to worry about him.

Arnulfo was driving a semi-truck by his fifteenth birthday. The owner would switch seats and allow Arnulfo to take a shift while he slept. The teen had experience as a farmer, construction worker, and with his father, shared a business selling vegetables from a bicycle cart. All went well until the gangs of Honduras began asking for their cut. Since every neighborhood and town had its own gang, this became untenable. Arnulfo finally refused, got into a fight where he was stabbed but survived, and his father told him to leave the country.

I showed him the house of a Virginia cousin who after a year had volunteered to sponsor him. Arnulfo asked me to navigate Google Earth so he could show me the tin shack his cousin grew up in. "The most humble house in Honduras," he stated and marveled at the three bedroom on a cul-de-sac that was now his cousin's Virginia home.

Arnulfo guaranteed his future through an act of bravery. Without money and always resourceful, he jumped on the *Bestia*, freight-hopping a train used by thousands to cross the length of Mexico.

It was a dangerous ride, and along the way, a girl fell asleep next to him, lost her grip and slipped under the train. His shelter roommates complained that this memory was a frequent nightmare that Arnulfo woke from with a yell.

And he was on the Bestia when one of the many criminals who stalked the train walked into his boxcar. Arnulfo described the man as tall, scarred, and well-armed. The thief pointed his gun at the group of kids huddled in the compartment and told Arnulfo's traveling companion to step forward. The man demanded everything he had on his person, and when the boy hesitated, the criminal fired his weapon. With the boy still dying, the murderer made Arnulfo carry the body to the top of the train and toss it.

When the train stopped at the next town, Arnulfo jumped off and asked locals about a place to stay. He was told there was a *casa de imigrantes* where he would find help. At that shelter, he slept on the floor with others traveling north, was fed, took a shower, and that same night, he spotted the man who murdered his friend. The tall figure was walking among sleeping migrants, looking for possible marks.

The next morning, Arnulfo went to the director of "the casa" and she called the police to report the murder. The police found the man, but Arnulfo was asked to identify him in person. They stood the handcuffed murderer a few feet in front of Arnulfo and asked him to sign a witness statement. Afterward, everyone praised Arnulfo's courage, and the police retrieved his friend's body. He was given a copy of his testimony, and that document would later provide grounds for a successful asylum request.

But terrified at that moment, Arnulfo disappeared from the Mexican shelter and took the most circuitous route to the U.S. he could improvise. He stayed far from the coast and big cities, imagining that somehow, he was being followed.

Once at the border, he jumped the fence and walked three days into the desert, attaching himself to a group of boys along the way. They got separated when a patrol found them, and during his escape, he fell into a cholla bush that left needles embedded along his backside. He was completely disoriented, and the cactus needles burned as he moved. Within a day he began hallucinating from thirst, and said that he was near dying in place, but he spotted a pool of yellow water with a floating dead cow. He drank knowing it might save him but would probably kill him. The next morning, he came upon a pregnant woman under a tree and decided he couldn't leave her. He found a road to wait for help.

A Tohono O'odham Indian picked him up and took both him and the woman to a clinic on the reservation. They pulled the needles off his back, and Arnulfo stayed for a day at his Indian savior's farm. The farmer advised him to wait for Border Patrol, but Arnulfo didn't trust that option. He thought it best to walk another day through the desert and find a town where he was sure he could find work. With the farm still visible, a helicopter spotted him walking alone, and within minutes, he was being chased by an agent on horseback. With one kick from the saddle, the agent sent him to a meeting with the desert floor.

Arnulfo says it was an indignation to be hogtied, but he admitted to giving them little choice. A few days later, he arrived at where he would spend the next year of his life.

Eleven

Like other fathers who were conscripted in the long Guatemalan civil war, Iran Cac-Xe's dad returned wounded, traumatized and abusive. At the end of third grade, Iran's father told him to quit school as he was too dumb to benefit from it. Iran refused and instead worked two jobs. He labored on his own farm and found a job in town making and selling street tacos. He paid for his schoolbooks and tuition, giving the rest to his mother. He was nine years old.

His father demanded military style discipline and had lists of chores that began before dawn. There were beatings if they weren't done to his satisfaction. Neighbors several times called the police and his father was jailed for domestic violence, but the police and judges were paid off, and he returned home within days. After the last fight with his father, a physical exchange that sent his father to the floor, Iran left the house and started walking north.

Strong and disciplined, used to work and study, he harbored a hunger to make something of himself and save his siblings—two sisters whom he treated like daughters. He cried on phone calls home and swore to his sisters that he would take care of them.

When the lawyers accepted his case for foster care, Iran asked for an extra phone call home. Trembling and shaking, he told his father that he had formally accused him of abuse in the United States. He asked his father to do the right thing and not deny what he had done, as this would stop any chance he had for asylum. I watched a bull of a boy whimper as he said he loved his father and would in time forgive him, but the truth was the truth.

On the trial date, Iran sat in a room with a juvenile court judge, his lawyers and the lawyers representing his parents. On a speakerphone were his mother and father. Iran's parents listened from Guatemala to the abuse charges, and his father was asked to offer a plea. He remained silent but present on the phone, neither accepting nor denying the charge. That was enough for a ruling.

Iran would spend another six months in the shelter, waiting for the legal process and his formal adoption through the juvenile courts.

And that was good for a six-year-old who was left at our doorstep by the immigration van. We did not take six-year-olds. We didn't have the toilets, classrooms, food, toys or clothing, but ICE said there was no choice. The stunned child was placed in a classroom with the oldest teens and immediately adopted by Iran Cac-Xe. They sat together in class, Iran showing him how to write and color and playing with him during recreation.

"I see my little sisters in him. I can't be there for them."

The case manager tried everything to find the child's parents, but unlike those rare and previous occasions when young children had been separated from a parent, ICE officials could offer little information. The child knew the name of his town, and first names of siblings, but that was all. It was distressing to all of us, and at that moment, we had yet to understand what was occurring.

Three weeks later, another ICE van arrived, this time loaded with young children, including a three-year-old who would end up in the shelter for a year. In a fast reconfiguration, we set up classrooms, activities, sought toys, and received quick training on new procedures. Howls rang out from the nursing office that told us they had started vaccinations. The cooks made special dishes, we reworked rules and thought through how to comfort a five-year-old with touching that was short of a hug.

The ten-year-olds became the "older kids" of this batch. Some of the new arrivals tantrummed, some kicked and bit, others cried, and most lost track of days. None understood where they were or what was happening. Without family contacts, they didn't receive phone calls.

Sometimes ICE helped, sometimes not. It depended on the day, the person asking and the person answering. It depended on the week's politics. It was the beginning of something awful.

Twelve

The rules of homeland security required that we not contact departed clients for at least one year. That included their parents and social media. And if we did, we forfeited the right to work in any government shelter. Fair enough.

It has been two years and many of the kids have found me. Most are still in school. One manages a Burger King, many work on farms or in construction. Others help in the family gardening business. One trains horses. I like seeing them on Facebook, especially the girls dancing in some Louisiana hamlet wearing traditional Mayan dresses.

The kids have started lives, they work hard, they send money to mom. Church and soccer are constants. A few are married. The children who had parents in the U.S. have assimilated into reconstituted families, with all that entails.

A deaf, mute girl has learned to sign and is on Instagram.

Like every group of poor immigrants before them, they are finding their way. All are scared and treading carefully.

As our nation ponders what to do about immigration, the children of Guatemala are most likely the last wave of immigrants from our hemisphere.

Mexico once sent millions, but the economy has modernized and more now go back then come over. We rarely saw Mexican children in the shelter. When we did, it was an exceptional circumstance involving a cartel that wanted land and took it. But there is opportunity in Mexico. People can get by and even do well.

We have all seen the images from Venezuela, its economy in a death spiral, with hunger, closed hospitals and desperate citizens. Yet, not a single kid from Venezuela appeared at our shelter. I'm sure there were a few at our sister shelters, but with the meltdown of an entire nation, you would assume a wave of refugees. But South American countries can take care of their own. Rather than venture the expensive and risky land route to the U.S., it is far safer for an economic refugee from

Venezuela to cross into Brazil or Chile and wait things out.

In Central America, Costa Rica and Panama have always been fine. Nicaragua struggles with its politics, but people aren't trying to flee en masse. It is still a country with an economy. El Salvador and Honduras once sent thousands, it's now a trickle. When I ask kids why, they say that if not for the gangs, even fewer would come north. The poverty and fear are real, but not what they once were. It takes a lot of pain before people will leave their families and what they know as home.

And that leaves Guatemala as the only country both close enough and poor enough to create migrants. It provided nearly all children in our shelter. However, and this is key, the kids were never from the city. It was the Indigenous countryside that sent its children.

Two thousand years ago, their Mayan ancestors suffered the environmentally driven collapse of a great civilization. It is repeating. Changing weather and primitive farming mean that people produce a dollar a day and live on whatever corn they can grow. It is simply not enough. Some argue that Guatemalans need to reduce their population, but we all know that families get smaller as opportunity improves and child mortality declines. Until then, families stay large.

Every Guatemalan child in our shelter expressed the same dream: if they could send twenty-five dollars a week to mom, their siblings could finish school and have meals without fail. Their parents might save for a little farmland, electricity or a medical treatment.

The best foreign aid has always been the children of a diaspora sending money home.

For the poorest, America's southern border is closed. They don't qualify to immigrate legally and crossing illegally has become forbidding: the border technology is impressive and the weather deadly. Few people make it across our southern desert. The last large group of immigrants willing to try are the kids from Guatemala. If history repeats, what they send to mom and pop will give Guatemala a future where its young people can stay home.

Our next dilemma may be what to do when none of our neighbors have children willing to endure all manner of hardship to find our soil. We may miss the "unskilled" desperate immigrants, and the restorative energy of their hungry, wide-eyed dreams.

Also by the Author

The Good Lessons:

A Teaching Life with Gangs, Delinquents & Troubled Teens

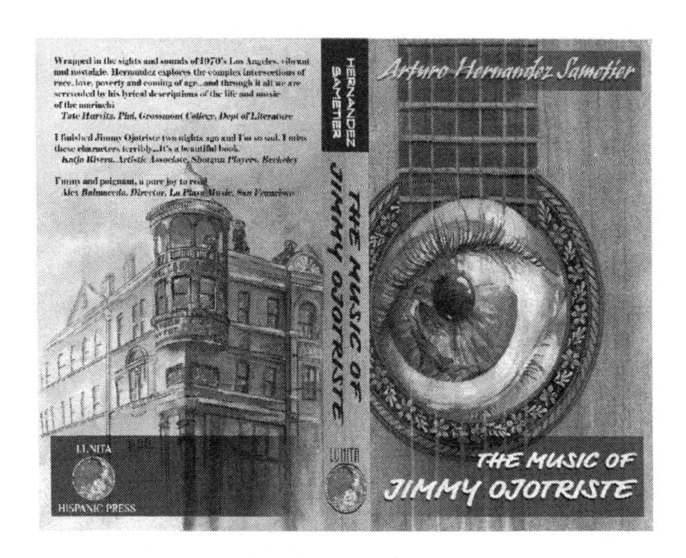

The Music of Jimmy Ojotriste

A lush, magical tale of street music, love and brujeria

The Cover Art for this book is from an original painting by

Esmeralda Piza

Please visit Lunitabooks.com for more information on the artist.

Arturo Hernandez-Sametier

Please visit Lunitabooks.com for more information on the author.

Made in the USA
Columbia, SC
10 October 2020

22529084R00062